BAXTER'S FINGER-PICKING, BLUES & RAGTIME MANUAL

BY
ROBERT BAXTER

BAXTER & SONS

Standard Book Number 8256 − 2606-4

© 1969 Amsco Music Publishing Company
33 West 60th Street, New York, N.Y. 10023

TABLE OF CONTENTS

INTRODUCTION

The tunes in this manual are some of my personal favorites. They have specific arrangements but as you become familiar with them they will change. The more they become a part of you, the more they will reflect your feelings about them.

It is difficult to arrive at specific tunes and arrangements for a collection, for the notes and tablature can only express a point in time. This is frustrating, because the very essence of these pieces is change and experimentation and freedom of interpretation. So rewrite the tunes if you like. Let your own ideas and stylistic traits mold the melodies to suit your own ears, but only after you have mastered the tunes as they are written. Changing tunes before you have mastered them only limits the number of new ideas and techniques you can learn from this manual. Avoiding or changing difficult passages instead of mastering them will, in the long run, slow your growth as a guitar player.

The instrumental solos in this manual may not be easy for you even if you already play in the styles mentioned. So be certain to read all the instructions at the beginning of the manual, following the rules and ideas carefully. If you have learned Finger-Picking or Blues on your own and this is the first Baxter & Son manual that you have used, I suggest that you go through Baxter's Finger-Picking Manual and gain a complete background for the tunes included in this manual.

i

Here is a list of performers I suggest hearing either live or on records in order to better understand and play the styles of songs in this book:

PINK ANDERSON	ROBERT JOHNSON
CHET ATKINS	JOHN KOERNER
ETTA BAKER	JIM KWESKIN JUG BAND
BLIND BLAKE	LEADBELLY
BIG BILL BROONZY	MANCE LIPSCOMB
IAN BUCHANAN	GEOFF MULDAUR
DAVE COHEN	SAM McGEE
RY COODER	BROWNIE McGHEE
ELIZABETH COTTEN	BLIND WILLIE McTELL
REV. GARY DAVIS	TOM PALEY
BLIND BOY FULLER	BERNARD PEARL
JESSE FULLER	DAVE RAY
FRANK HAMILTON	DAVE VAN RONK
LIGHTNIN' HOPKINS	DICK ROSMINI
SON HOUSE	JOSEPH SPENCE
MISSISSIPPI JOHN HURT	MERLE TRAVIS
LIL' SON JACKSON	DOC WATSON
SKIP JAMES	BUKKA WHITE
LEMON JEFFERSON	ETC., ETC., ETC....

THE TABLATURE AND MUSIC NOTATION USED IN THIS MANUAL

All the Finger-Picking, Ragtime and Blues pieces in this manual are written in two ways, both in Normal Music Notation and in our own Tablature System (BAXTAB). Whichever method you use, it is suggested that you acquaint yourself with the rudiments of Finger-Picking as given in Baxter's Finger-Picking Manual. The more familiar you are with the technical and stylistic traits of Finger-Picking Style, as outlined in the Finger-Picking Manual, the more correct and authentic the pieces in this manual will sound.

BAXTAB

Our Tablature System is a short-hand supplied primarily for non-music-readers who prefer an easy-to-use system for reading and writing music. However, music-readers will find the tablature helpful in discovering the proper fingering of passages. Every tenth measure is numbered in the music and tablature versions for cross-reference.

Slashes, Bar Lines, Off-Beat And On-Beat Melody

BAXTAB uses numbers to express which strings are to be played. "6, 5" and "4" refer to the Bass Strings of the guitar. "1, 2" and "3" refer to the Trebles. Normally, the thumb plays the bass strings in Finger-Picking and Blues styles, and the index plays the treble strings. Some players prefer, however, to play the 1st string with the middle finger and reserve the index for the 2nd and 3rd strings.

In BAXTAB measures are divided by bar lines (|) and beats (foot-taps) are indicated by slashes (/). A typical bass string pattern would be indicated as follows:

```
                              /   /   /   /  ←——— beats (foot-taps)
       chord ——→ C
       bar line ——→ |  5 ,  4 ,  5 ,  4 |  ←——— bar line
```

Each unit of sound is separated by a comma. In the above example, the thumb plays a basic alternating pattern.

A "pinch" is simple to recognize: two numbers placed together and set off from the rest of the tablature by commas. On the opposite page "52" = play the 5th string with the thumb and the 2nd string with the index finger in unison. Normally, in a "pinch" the thumb plays a bass string and the index plays a treble string, but in some pieces in this manual a pinch might be "31,"etc. In this case the thumb plays the 3rd string and the index plays the 1st string. Also the thumb can play treble string notes that fall on-the-beat, or bass notes that fall off-the-beat.

```
        /         /         /         /
     C
     | 52    ,    4    ,    31    ,    3 |
    thumb-index  thumb  thumb-index   thumb
                            or
                        thumb-middle
```

Numbers given between beats should be played e v e n l y :

```
       /         /         /         /
    C
    | 5 , 2 , 4 , 1 , 5 , 2 , 4 , 1 |
```

Below, two notes must be played evenly between each bass beat:

```
       /               /               /               /
    C
    | 5 , 2 , 1 , 4 , 3 , 2 , 5 , 2 , 1 , 4 , 3 , 2 |
```

Parenthesis

A parenthesis in the tablature indicates a change in the fingering of the chord you are in.

C
41   = in a C chord, pinch the 4th and 1st strings
        in unison.

C
41(3) = pinch the 4th and 1st strings in unison, as
        above, but add a finger of the left hand to
        the 1st string at the 3rd fret. The number
        in parenthesis refers to the fret number.
        The parenthesis refers only to the string
        immediately preceeding it. The Rest Of
        The Chord Should Remain As Intact As
        Possible. The chord is fingered normally
        for the next notes.

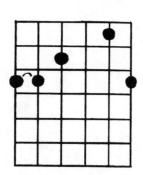

C, with the 1st
string fretted
at the 3rd fret

G
41(0) = pinch the 4th and 1st strings in the usual
        manner, but take the fretting finger off the
        1st string. The 1st string is played "open,"
        "(0)" or un-fretted. The Rest Of The Chord
        Should Remain Intact. The fretting finger
        should be replaced when the pinch has been
        completed.

G, with the
1st string open

G

5(0)1 = pinch the 5th and 1st strings in the usual man-

ner, but take the fretting finger off the 5th

string. The 5th string is played "open," "(0)"

or un-fretted. Remember, a parenthesis

refers only to the string number Directly

Preceeding It. The rest of the chord should

remain intact. The fretting finger should

be replaced when the pinch has been com-

pleted.

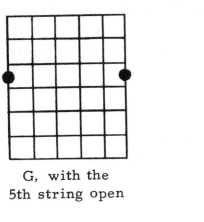

G, with the
5th string open

A parenthesis may also be used after a chord:

D(3)   = the entire D chord is to be moved up 3 frets

from where it is normally played.

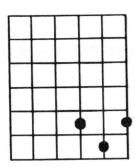

D(3) or F

Hammer-on's, Slides, Pull-off's and Stretches

Hammer-on's are indicated as follows: "3(0) H(1)" = play the 3rd string open (un-fretted) and then hammer-on the string at the 1st fret. Some examples of hammer-on's are:

```
 /      /
3(0) H (1)  =  play the 3rd string open on the 1st beat, and then hammer-
               on so the 2nd tone of the hammer-on sounds out where
               indicated.


  /              /
52(0) H (1) , 4  =  pinch the 5th string and the open 2nd string, ham-
                    mering-on the 2nd string at the 1st fret. The 2nd tone
                    of the hammer-on should sound out between the beats.


 /               /
3(0) H (1) , 1 , 5  =  pluck the 3rd string open on the beat, hammer-on
                       and then play the 1st string, followed by a bass
                       beat on the 5th string. The two notes played be-
                       tween the beats (the hammer-on and the normally
                       plucked 1st string) should be played evenly.
```

An arrow (———➤) indicates a slide. A slide may join one note to another:

```
   /      /    /       /                /     /    /      /
  G                                    C
| 63  ,   4 ,  6  ,  4(0)2(3)➤(5), 1(0)| 5  ,  4 ,  5  ,  4 |
```

Or a slide may join one chord to another:

```
        /            /
      A♭6th ———➤ A6th
       42    ,    5
```

A "P" in a parenthesis indicates a "pull-off."

An "S" indicates that the string should be stretched or choked.

This symbol will be found before a multi-noted pinch. It indicates that the strings should be played in a quick arpeggio. The strings are to be played almost, but not quite, simultaneously. The strings should be played from bass to treble, unless otherwise indicated.

THE
MUSIC
NOTATION

Standard music notation for the guitar is used in this manual, but a few special signs are employed to express certain techniques. Some of these signs, such as the symbol for a multi-noted pinch (   ), are the same in the music notation and BAXTAB. Symbols which are found only in the music notation, and BAXTAB symbols which are expressed a bit differently in the music notation are given below.

A diamond-shaped note (♦) indicates a harmonic. The harmonic symbol is placed on the line or space of the staff corresponding to the open value of the string to be played. The fret number is given to indicate where the harmonic should be played:

HARM. (12)

◊

A hammer-on is indicated by " H. "

A pull-off is indicated by " P."

A stretched or choked string is indicated by .

A slide is indicated by the symbol .

A small circle above a note () indicates that the note is found on an open string. A small number in a circle next to a note (②) indicates the string on which the note is played.

❧❧❧❧❧❧❧

By the way, if you need to brush up on musical notation, Baxter's Accompaniment Manual will help you. It has a chapter devoted to teaching guitarists how to read music.

AN IMPORTANT
WORD FOR BOTH
TABLATURE AND
MUSIC READERS

The special sound of Blues is difficult to attain without studying the style first-hand. However, a few concepts might help you in playing the pieces in this manual ... and understanding something about the special timing of Blues tunes.

Most of the time, Finger - Picking and related guitar styles are played and written in 4/4 time. You would think that 4/4 time Finger-Picking, Ragtime and Blues pieces would follow the rules of standard 4/4 time duple (double) meter music. That is, the thumb would pluck on the beat, while the syncopated notes would fall evenly, directly between the beats (as illustrated below):

In the authentic playing of Finger-Picking, Ragtime and Blues pieces, although the music is written (and played) in 4/4, it is timed as if it were written in trochaic (triple) meter. That is, the timing allows for the playing of two syncopated melody notes between the beats:

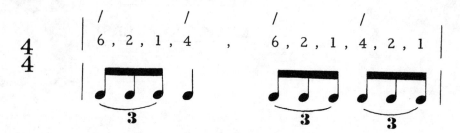

However, in the styles in which we're concerned, only one melody note is usually played between the bass beats. This off-beat melody note is timed as if it were the third division of each beat. The second division of the beat is silent. In tablature, dashes are used to indicate a silence which should be counted but not played:

The whole idea, as you can see, is that each beat gets three counts, and notes are played only on the first and third counts. This gives the typical rocking rhythm which is characteristic to the authentic sound of Finger-Picking, Ragtime and Blues.

BLUES TIMING SYMBOLS

Since Finger-Picking, Blues and Ragtime songs are based on triplets, both the tablature and music notation would be cluttered if the normal signs were used. The music notation would use ♪ ⅄ ♪ and the tablature would be filled with dashes to indicate the silent second unit of each beat: 6 , — , 2 , 4 . So, all the songs in this manual, except Winding Boy, use a shorthand method of expressing triplets.

In tablature the triplet meter is indicated:

$$
\begin{array}{ccc}
/ & / & \\
6 , 2 , 4 & = & 6 , — , 2 , 4
\end{array}
$$

In music notation the triplet meter is indicated:

♫ = ♪ ⅄ ♪

Whenever a piece uses this shorthand it is given at the beginning of both the tablature and music notation versions.

FRANKLIN BLUES

BY SAM MCGEE

This excellent Finger-Picking tune has been a favorite of mine for a long time, mainly due to the Sam McGee "touch" of building a novel melody within the confines of a familiar chord progression. Franklin Blues is one of the first songs that kindled my interest in Finger-Picking and laid the foundation of my own personal style. Perhaps it will do the same for you.

Excellent examples of the playing of Sam McGee can be found on the Folkways recording, "The McGee Brothers & Arthur Smith." Well worth listening to.

The tablature indicates the word "damp" below certain notes. This means that the notes should be played as usual, but the fingers of the chording hand should release their pressure on the strings the moment after the strings are plucked. The fingers themselves should not come off the strings, but, rather, lightly rest on the strings to kill the tone. In the music notation a damp is indicated by a dot directly under the note to be dampened (♪).

A6th

F

G

D

C

G7th

Chords used in

Franklin Blues

FRANKLIN BLUES
By Sam McGee

Lively

/   /   /   /
5 , 2 , 4   =   5 , — , 2 , 4

(1)

A6th ⟶ A6th(3)   F

$\frac{4}{4}$ 2 | 43 , 1(8) , 31 , 2 , 43 , 4 , 32 , 5(3) | 41 , 1(3) , 31 , 2 ,

G   C

5(3)3 , 4 , 32 , 6 | 52 , 3(3) , 42 , 2(3) , 61(0) , 1 , 4 , 5 | 41 , 2(4) ,

A6th ➤ A6th(3)   F

31 , 1(3) , 5 , 4 , 2 | 43 , 1(8) , 31 , 2 , 43 , 4 , 32 , 5(3) | 41 , 1(3) ,

C   G   C

31 , 2 , 5(3)3 , 4 | 51 , 2(4) , 41 , 62 , 3(3) , 42 | 52 , 3(2) , 3(0) ,

(10)

F(2)   A6th(3)

4(2) , 5 , 4 | 5(5) , 31 , 2 , 41 , 2 , 3 , 2 | 41 , 421(8) , 321(8) , 5(4) |
                                                            (damp)

D   A6th   F

/   /   /   /   /   /   /   /

4 , 31 , 2 , 41 , 4 , 31 , 2 | 31 , 421(5) , 321(5) , 1(0) | 61 , 41 ,
                               (damp)

                 C   G

       /   /   /   /   /   /   /

1(3) , 61 , 2 , 43 | 51 , 2(4) , 41 , 5 , 41(3) , 4 | 51 , 2(4) , 41 , 62 ,

                 C   A6th→A6th(3)   F

       /   /   /   /   /   /   /

3(3) , 42 | 52 , 6(3) , 5 , 4 , 2 | 43 , 1(8) , 31 , 2 , 43 , 4 , 32 , 5(3) |

                                       G

/   /   /   /   /   /   /

41 , 1(3) , 31 , 2 , 5(3)3 , 4 , 32 , 6 | 52 , 3(3) , 42 , 2(3) , 61(0) ,

(20)

               C   A6th→A6th(3)

     /   /   /   /   /   /   /

1 , 4 , 5 | 41 , 2(4) , 31 , 1(3) , 5 , 4 , 2 | 43 , 1(8) , 31 , 2 , 43 ,

            F   C   G

       /   /   /   /   /   /   /   /

4 , 32 , 5(3) | 41 , 1(3) , 31 , 2 , 5(3)3 , 4 | 51 , 2(4) , 41 , 62 , 3(3) ,

(G) C
                                              G7th

/   /   /   /   /   /   /   /   /

42 | 52 , 3(2) , 3(0) , 4(2) , 5 , 4 | 51 , 4 , 61 , 4 , 1(3) ⟶ (5) , 1(3) ,

                                    F

/   /   /   /   /   /   /   /   /

1(0) , 2(3) , 1(0) , 3(3) , 2(0) , 3 | 62 , 31(3) , 61 , 4 | 61 , 41 , 1(3) ,

(30)

               C   G

/   /   /   /   /   /   /   /

61 , 2 , 43 | 51 , 2(4) , 41 , 5 , 41(3) , 4 | 51 , 2(4) , 41 , 62 , 3(3) ,

       C

/   /   /   /   /

42 | 52 , 6(3) , 5 , — ‖

FRANKLIN BLUES
By Sam McGee

●●●

Giving names to tunes is a tricky business. If you name a tune after a friend, all your other friends hate you. If you name a tune after a thing like "tennis elbow" people think you're corny or being cute. If you simply give a tune a number like "Opus 17" everyone calls you up and wants to hear Opus 1, Opus 2, and Opus 3 and so on. When I first named this piece I took the "cute" approach, unfortunately. I named it "Dirty Rag." However, when I typed out the letter "R" of "R-A-G" on the typewriter, my finger slipped and fell on the "B." So now I had "Dirty B...." What word would be good that begins with a "B?" I arrived at Banana. So there I had the title... Dirty Banana. Ever since then I have felt terrible. What a crummy name for a song. Ivanho-Ho Rag is much better.

●●●

IVANHO-HO RAG

BY ROBERT BAXTER

Chords used
in
Ivanho-Ho Rag

G

F♯Dim

C

Dm

F

OPEN

A6th

C7th

IVANHO-HO RAG
By Robert Baxter

$$\frac{/}{5}, 2, \overset{/}{4} = \overset{/}{5}, -, 2, \overset{/}{4}$$

_____

(1)

G

$\frac{4}{4}$ $\overset{/}{-}$, 3 , $\overset{/}{3(1)}$ H (2) , 3 , $\overset{/}{61}$, 1(2) , $\overset{/}{4}$, 1(1) | $\overset{/}{6}$, 3 , $\overset{/}{3(1)}$ H (2) , 3 ,

$\overset{/}{61}$, 1(2) , $\overset{/}{4}$, 1(1) | $\overset{/}{6}$, 3 , 2(3)→(5) , $\overset{F\sharp}{dim}$ $\overset{G}{\overset{/}{1(0)}}$, 31 , $\overset{C}{\overset{/}{1}}$, 3 , 1 | $\overset{/}{5}$, 3 ,

F♯
dim   G   C   G

2(3)→(5) , 1(0) , $\overset{/}{31}$, 1 , $\overset{/}{3}$, 1 | $\overset{/}{5}$, 3 , $\overset{/}{3(1)}$ H (2) , 3 , 61 , $\overset{/}{1(2)}$,

$\overset{/}{4}$, 1(1) | $\overset{/}{6}$, 3 , $\overset{/}{3(1)}$ H (2) , 3 , 61 , 1(2) , $\overset{/}{4}$, 1(1) | $\overset{/}{6}$, 3 , $\overset{/}{2(3)}$→(5) ,

F♯
dim   G   C   A6th   Dm   F

1(0) , $\overset{/}{31}$, 1 , $\overset{/}{3}$, 1 | $\overset{/}{5}$, $\overset{/}{4}$, $\overset{/}{51(5)}$, 1(3) , $\overset{/}{4}$, 2 | $\overset{/}{51}$, $\overset{/}{4}$, $\overset{/}{62}$, 1 , $\overset{/}{4}$, 2 |

(10)

(F)   OPEN   A6th   A6th(3)

61(3) , 1 , 4 , 2(3)→(5) , 1(3) H (5) , 1(3) , 2 , 1 , 3 | 5 , 4 , 4(7)2(6) ,

F♯
dim   OPEN   C   C7th
                                                            (2)

1(5) , 2(6) , 42 , 1 | 4(4)2(1) , 4(3) , 2(0) , 5 , 42 , — | 53 , 2 , 41 ,

                                                              F(2)

3 , 6(5)2 , 1 , 43 , 2 | 51 , 3 , 42 , 6(5)1 , 42 | 63 , 2 , 41 , 3 , 62 ,

                                                       C7th
                                                          (2)

1 , 43 , 2 | 61 , 3 , 42 , 61 , 42 | 53 , 2 , 41 , 3 , 6(5)2 , 1 , 43 , 2 |

                                                      F♯
                              A6th(3)   dim   OPEN

51 , 3 , 42 , 6(5)1 , 42 | 4(7)2(6) , 1(5) , 2(6) , 42 , 1 , 4(4)2(1) ,

(20)

                        C

4(3) , 2(0) , 5 | 42 , — , — , — ‖

IVANHO-HO RAG
By Robert Baxter

24

POLICEDOG BLUES

BY ARTHUR "BLIND" BLAKE

This song in "Open - D Tuning" was first introduced to many of us by the incredible Ry Cooder. Since then it has become one of my favorite Finger - Picking Blues pieces. Although <u>Policedog</u> is mainly an accompaniment to the singing of Blake, the complexity of the tune makes it an excellent guitar solo.

The tuning for the guitar is, counting from the bass 6th string, D - A - D - F♯ - A - D. In order to get into this tuning a revised version of the "matching method" of tuning the guitar can be used. Simply tune the 6th string down one whole note to D and then match the strings according to the following diagram:

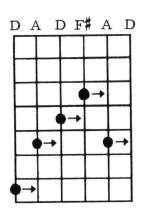

With the 6th string tuned down to D: the 5th string open equals the 6th string fretted at the 7th fret, and so on.

As with other tunes in this manual, whenever you play a pinch that incorporates two bass or two treble strings, the thumb plays the lowest string (tone wise) and the index plays the more treble of the two strings. Also, the thumb plays treble strings which fall on the beat.

In this song harmonics are called for ... in the music by diamond - shaped notes (♦) and in the tablature by the word Harm. In the tablature, the fret where the harmonic is played is indicated by a number in parenthesis and in the music notation it is indicated above the notes. (Remember, the term fret applies to the wire, not to the space.) The harmonic is played by placing a finger lightly on the string to be played directly above the fret called for. The fretting finger should barely touch the string. The finger should be exactly above the fret wire, neither to the left or right of it. The string when plucked close to the bridge should produce a bell-like sound, rather than the normal string sound.

Chords used in Policedog Blues

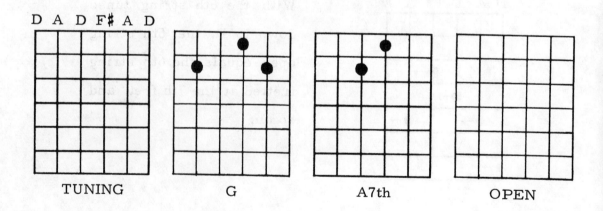

D A D F♯ A D

TUNING   G   A7th   OPEN

POLICEDOG BLUES
By Blind Blake

guitar tuning (6th to 1st string): D A D F♯ A D

/   /   /   /
5 , 2 , 4 = 5 , — , 2 , 4

---

(1)

HARM. (12)   OPEN
4 / / / /   /   /   / /   / / / /   / /   /
4 4, 1, 2, 3 | 4, 1, —, 2, 3 | 4, 1, 2, 3 | 4, 1, —, 2, 3, 5(1) |

G   OPEN
  /   /   /   /   /   /
 5(2) , 2 , 41 , 2 , 61(3S) , 1 , 4 , 2(0) | 1(3)→(2) P (0) , 2(2) , 1 ,

/   /   /   /   /   /   /   /   /
2 , 4(3) , 3 , 4 | 6 , 1 , 2(3) , 2(2) , 2 , 4(3) , 3 , 4 | 6 , 1 , 4 , 2 , 61 ,

(10)

     A7th   G   A7th   OPEN
/   /   /   /   /   /   /   /   /   /
4 | 5 , 3 , 2 , 2(3S) , — , 2 , 4 | 5 , 3 , 2 , 3 , 5 , 3 , 2 , 3 | 6 , 1 , 2(3) ,

         /   /   /   /   /   /   /   /   /   /
2(2) , 2 , 4(3) , 3 , 4 | 6 , 1 , 4 , 2 , 61 , 4 | 6 , 1(7) , 4 , 2(8S) , 61(7) , 4 |

29

(OPEN)   HARM. (12)
/   /   /   /   /   /   /   /   /   /   /
6 , 1(7) , 4 , 2(8S) , 61(7) , 41(9)—→(12) │ 6(0) , 1 , 2 , 3 │ 4 , 1 , — ,

        OPEN G   OPEN
/   /   /   │   /   /   /   /   /   /
2 , 3 , 5(1) │ 5(2) , 2 , 41 , 2 , 61(3S) , 1 , 4 , 2(0) │ 1(3)—→(2) P (0) ,

                                                                              (20)

/   /   /   │ /   /   /   /   │ /
2(2) , 1 , 2 , 4(3) , 3 , 4 │ 6 , 1 , 2(3) , 2(2) , 2 , 4(3) , 3 , 4 │ 6 , 1 ,

                A7th   G   A7th
/   /   /   /   /   │ /   /   /   /
4 , 2 , 61 , 4 │ 5 , 3 , 2 , 2(3S) , — , 2 , 4 │ 5 , 3 , 2 , 3 , 5 , 3 ,

        OPEN
/   │ /   /   /   /   │ /   /   /   /
2 , 3 │ 6 , 1 , 2(3) , 2(2) , 2 , 4(3) , 3 , 4 │ 6 , 1 , 4 , 2 , 61 , 4│

/   /   /   /   /   │ /
43 , 4(2) 3(1) , 4(3) 3(2) , 4(4) 3(3) , 43 , — , 6 │ 43 , 4(2) 3(1) ,

(OPEN)

／
4(3) 3(2) , 4(4) 3(3) , 43 , — , 6 ┃ 43 , 4(2) 3(1) , 4(3) 3(2) , 4(4) 3(3) , 43 ,

／   ／   ／   ／   ／

4(2) 3(1) , 4(3) 3(2) , 4(4) 3(3) ┃ 43 , ⟶ 4(2) 3(1) , 4(4) 3(3) , 43 , — , 5(1)┃
／   ／   ／   ／   4(2)3(1)   ／   ／   ／

(30)

G   OPEN
／   ／   ／   ／   ／
5(2) , 2 , 41 , 2 , 61(3S) , 1 , 4 , 2(0) ┃ 1(3) ⟶ (2) <u>P</u> (0) , 2(2) , 1 , 2 ,
                                          ／   ／   ／   ／

／   ／   ／   ／   ／   ／   ／   ／
4(3) , 3 , 4 ┃ 6 , 1 , 2(3) , 2(2) , 2 , 4(3) , 3 , 4 ┃ 6 , 1 , 4 , 2 , 61 , 4┃

A7th   G   A7th   OPEN
／   ／   ／   ／ ／ ／   ／   ／   ／   ／
5 , 3 , 2 , 2(3S) , — , 2 , 4 ┃ 5 , 3 , 2 , 3 , 5 , 3 , 2 , 3 ┃ 6 , 1 ,

／   ／   ／   ／   ／   ／   ／   ／   ／
2(3) , 2(2) , 2 , 4(3) , 3 , 4 ┃ 6 , 1 , 4 , 2 , 61 , 4 ┃ 64 , 6(2) 4(2) ,

31

(OPEN)

/   /   /   /   /   /   /

6(3)4(3) , 6(4)4(4) , 4 | 6 , 6(2)4(2) , 6(3)4(3) , 6(4)4(4) , 4 | 6 , 4 , 6 ,

(40)

/   /   /   /   /

6(2) , 4(2) , 6(3) , 4(3) , 6(4) , 4(4) | 6 , 4 , 6 , 6(2) , 4(2) , 6(2) ,

                                     G   OPEN

/   /   /   /   /   /

6(3) , 4(3) , 6(3) , 6(4) , 4(4) , 5 | 5(2) , 2 , 41 , 2 , 61(3S) , 1 , 4 , 2(0) |

/   /   /   /   /   /   /

1(3) → (2) P (0) , 2(2) , 1 , 2 , 4(3) , 3 , 4 | 6 , 1 , 2(3) , 2(2) , 2 , 4(3) ,

                                  A7th   G

/   /   /   /   /   /   /   /

3 , 4 | 6 , 1 , 4 , 2 , 61 , 4 | 5 , 3 , 2 , 2(3S) , — , 2 , 4 | 5 , 3 ,

       A7th   OPEN

/   /   /   /   /   /   /

2 , 3 , 5 , 3 , 2 , 3 | 6 , 1 , 2(3) , 2(2) , 2 , 4(3) , 3 , 4 |

(OPEN)   G   OPEN

/   /   /   /   /   /   /   /

6 , 1 , 4 , 2 , 61 , 4 | 5(2) , 2 , 41 , 2 , 61(3S) , 1 , 4 , 2(0) |

(50)

/   /   /   /   /   /   /

1(3) → (2) $\underline{P}$ (0) , 2(2) , 1 , 2 , 4(3) , 3 , 4 | 6 , 1 , 2(3) , 2(2) , 2 , 4(3) ,

                                  A7th   G

/   /   /   /   /   /   /   /   /

3 , 4 | 6 , 1 , 4 , 2 , 61 , 4 | 5 , 3 , 2 , 2(3S) , — , 2 , 4 | 5 , 3 ,

    A7th   OPEN

/   /   /   /   /   /   /   /

2 , 3 , 5 , 3 , 2 , 3 | 6 , 2(5) , 1(3) , 2(4) , 1 , 3(5) , 2 , 4 | 3 , 4(5) ,

           HARM. (12)

/   /   /   /

3 , 4 , 6 , 4321   ‖

POLICEDOG BLUES
By Blind Blake

CANDYMAN BLUES

BY MISSISSIPPI JOHN HURT

This tune, transcribed directly from the playing of the late Mississippi John Hurt, is one of the most requested of all the tunes he made famous during his lifetime. His marvelous renditions of Creole Belle, Casey Jones, Frankie, Spoonful, Spike Driver's Blues and Candyman have become a part of every serious guitar picker's repertoire. Mississippi John Hurt's music and gentle smile will never be forgotten.

↓ = brush down over the strings.

 = pluck "2(2)," as noted, and hammer-on "2(3)" so that this second tone of the hammer-on falls on the same beat as the "4." The "4" is plucked by the thumb as usual.

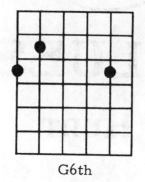

G6th

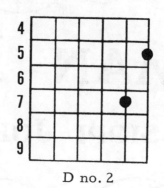

4
5
6
7
8
9

D no. 2

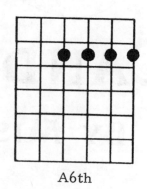

A6th

Chords used in

Candyman Blues

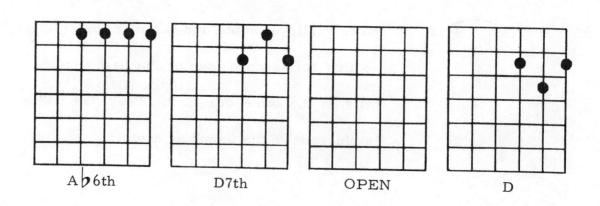

A♭6th   D7th   OPEN   D

CANDYMAN BLUES
By Mississippi John Hurt

Transcribed By Howard Berg

(straight duple meter)

_____

(1)

A6th

4/4 6 | 5 , 42 , 5 , 2(2) ‿H‿ 42(3) | 52(2) H‿(3) , 4 , 2 , 5 , 6 |

5 , 42 , 5 , 2(2) ‿H‿ 42(3) | 52(2) H‿(3) , 4 , 2 , 5 , 5(4) |

G6th   A6th

5 , 42 , 5 , 1 , 4 , 2 | 51(4) , 2 , 41 , 1(4) , 5 , 1 , 4 , 3 |

5 , 41(5) , 5 , 1(5) , 4 , 2 | 51(5) , 4 , 5(4) , 5(3) |

(10)

G6th   A6th

5 , 42 , 5 , 1 , 4 , 2 | 51(4) , 2 , 41 , 1(4) , 5 , 1 , 4 , 3 |

41

(A6th)

/   /   /   /   /   /   /   /   /
5 , 41(5) , 5 , 1(5) , 4 , 2 | 51(5) , 4 , 5 , 6 | 5 , 42 ,

              H
/   ⌒ /   /   /   /   /   /
5 , 2(2) , 42(3) | 52(2) H (3) , 4 , 2 , 5 , 6 | 5 , 42 ,

              H   G6th
/   ⌒ /   /   /   /   /   /
5 , 2(2) , 42(3) | 52(2) H (3) , 4 , 2 , 5 , 5(4) | 5 , 42 , 5 , 1 ,

                                                 A6th
/   /   /   /   /   /   /   /
4 , 2 | 51(4) , 2 , 41 , 1(4) , 5 , 1 , 4 , 3 | 5 , 41(5) ,

(20)

                                                 G6th
/   /   /   /   /   /   /   /
5 , 1(5) , 4 , 2 | 51(5) , 4 , 5(4) , 5(3) | 5 , 42 , 5 , 1 ,

/   /   /   /   /   /
4 , 2 | 51(4) , 2 , 41 , 1(4) , 5 , — , 2(3)→(5) , 41 |

Ab6th → A6th   A6th → A6th(7)

/   /   /   /   /   /   /   /   /
52 , 4 , 3 , 5 , 4 | 5 , 1(5) , 4 , 51(5) , 4 , 2 | 4 ,

/   /   /   /   /
31(12) , 4 , 1(12) , 3 , 2 | 41(12) , 3 , 1(10) , 4 , 1(12) ,

/   /   /   /   /   /   /   /
3 , 2 | 4 , 31(12) , 4 , 1(10) , 3 | 41(12) , 3 , 1(10) , 4 ,

(30)

OPEN D(7)

         /   /   /   /   /   /
1(12) , 3 , 2 | 4 , 321 , 4 , 21 , 3 , 2 | 41 , 2 , 3 , 1 ,

        D no. 2   D7th(4)

/   /   /   /   /   /   /
4 , 2 , 3 | 4 , 321 , 4 , 2 , 3 | 41(0) , 2 , 3 , 1(0) , 4 ,

     D7th(2)   A6th

    /   /   /   /   /   /   /   /
2 , 3 | 41(0) , 2 , 3 , 1(0) , 4 , 2 , 3 | 5 , 42 , 5(4) , 5(3) |

G6th

/   /   /   /   /   /
5 , 42 , 5 , 1 , 4 , 2 | 51(4) , 2 , 41 , 1(4) , 5 , 1 ,

A6th

/   /   /   /   /   /   /
4 , 3 | 5 , 41(5) , 5 , 1(5) , 4 , 2 | 51(5) , 4 , 5 , 6 |

(40)

/   /   /   H   /   /   /   /   /
5 , 42 , 5 , 2(2) , 42(3) | 52(2) H (3) , 4 , 2 , 5 , 6 | 5 ,

G6th

/   /   H   /   /   /   /   /   /
42 , 5 , 2(2) , 42(3) | 52(2) H (3) , 4 , 2 , 5 , 5(4) | 5 , 42 ,

A6th

/   /   /   /   /   /   /
5 , 1 , 4 , 2 | 51(4) , 2 , 41 , 1(4) , 5 , 1 , 4 , 3 |

/   /   /   /   /   /   /
5 , 41(5) , 5 , 1(5) , 4 , 2 | 51(5) , 4 , 5(4) , 5(3) |

G6th
/   /   /   /   /   /
5 , 42 , 5 , 1 , 4 , 2 | 51(4) , 2 , 41 , 1(4) , 5 , 1 ,

(50)

A6th
/   /   /   /   /   /
4 , 3 | 5 , 41(5) , 5 , 1(5) , 4 , 2 | 51(5) , 4 , 5 , 1(5) ,

/   /   /   /   /
4 , 2 | 4(4) , 1(5) , 4(4) , 4(3) , 1(5) , 4(3) | 4 , 1(5) , 4 , 2 ,

                                G6th   A6th
/   /   /   /   /   /
5(4) , 3 , 5(3) , 3(0) | 5 , 42 , 5 , 1(4) , 4 , 3 | 5 , 1(5) ,

/   /   /   /   /   /
4 , 51(5) , 4 , 2 | 4(4) , 1(5) , 4(4) , 4(3) , 1(5) , 4(3) |

                                                      G6th
/   /   /   /   /   /   /
4 , 1(5) , 4 , 2 , 5(4) , 3 , 5(3) , 3(0) | 5 , 42 , 5 , 1 , 4 , 2 |

45

(G6th)
   /   /   /   A♭6th ⟶ A6th

51(4) , 2 , 41 , 1(4) , 5 , — , 2(3)⟶(5) , 41 | 52 , 4 ,

(60)

                                           A6th ⟶ A6th(7)

3 , 5 , 4 | 5 , 1(5) , 4 , 51(5) , 4 , 2 | 4 , 31(12) ,

4 , 1(12) , 3 , 2 | 41(12) , 3 , 1(10) , 4 , 1(12) , 3 , 2 |

4 , 31(12) , 4 , 1(10) , 3 | 41(12) , 3 , 1(10) , 4 , 1(12) ,

      OPEN   D(7)

3 , 2 | 4 , 321 , 4 , 21 , 3 , 2 | 41 , 2 , 3 , 1 , 4 , 2 , 3 |

D no. 2   D7th(4)

4 , 321 , 4 , 2 , 3 | 41(0) , 2 , 3 , 1(0) , 4 , 2 , 3 |

(70)

D7th(2)

/   /   /   /   A6th / / / /

41(0) , 2 , 3 , 1(0) , 4 , 2 , 3 | 5 , 42 , 5(4) , 5(3) |

G6th

/   /   /   /   /   /   /

5 , 42 , 5 , 1 , 4 , 2 | 51(4) , 2 , 41 , 1(4) , 5 , 1 ,

A6th

/   /   /   /   / / / /

4 , 3 | 5 , 41(5) , 5 , 1(5) , 4 , 2 | 51(5) , 4 , 5 , 6 |

                            H

/   /   /   /   / / / /

5 , 42 , 5 , 2(2) , 42(3) | 52(2) H (3) , 4 , 2 , 5 , 6 |

                            H

/   /   /   /   / / / /

5 , 42 , 5 , 2(2) , 42(3) | 52(2) H (3) , 4 , 2 , 5 , 5(4) |

(80)

G6th   A6th

/ / /   /   /   /   /   /

5 , 42 , 5 , 1 , 4 , 2 | 51(4) , 2 , 41 , 1(4) , 5 , 1 , 4 , 3 |

47

(A6th)

/   /   /   /   /   /   /   /
5 , 41(5) , 5 , 1(5) , 4 , 2 | 51(5) , 4 , 5(4) , 5(3) |

G6th   A6th

/   /   /   /   /   /   /   /
5 , 42 , 5 , 1 , 4 , 2 | 51(4) , 2 , 41 , 1(4) , 5 , 1 , 4 , 3 |

/   /   /   /   /   /   /   /
5 , 41(5) , 5 , 1(5) , 4 , 2 | 51(5) , 4 , 5 , 1(5) , 4 , 2 |

/   /   /   /   /   /
4(4) , 1(5) , 4(4) , 4(3) , 1(5) , 4(3) | 4 , 1(5) , 4 , 2 ,

(90)

                      G6th   A6th

/   /   /   /   /   /   /   /
5(4) , 3 , 5(3) , 3(0) | 5 , 42 , 5 , 1(4) , 4 , 3 | 5 , 1(5) ,

/   /   /   /   /   /   /
4 , 51(5) , 4 , 2 | 4(4) , 1(5) , 4(4) , 4(3) , 1(5) , 4(3) |

(A6th)   G6th

/   /   /   /   /   /
4 , 1(5) , 4 , 2 , 5(4) , 3 , 5(3) , 3(0) | 5 , 42 , 5 , 1 ,

                                                          A6th

/   /   /   /   /   /
4 , 2 | 51(4) , 2 , 41 , 1(4) , 5 , 1 , 4 , 3 | 5 , 41(5) ,

/   /   /   /   /
5 , 1(5) , 4 , 2 | 51(5) , 4 , 5 , 1(5) , 4 , 2 | 4(4) , 1(5) ,

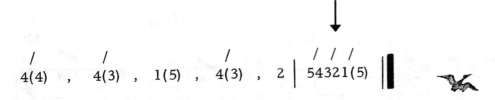

/   /   /   /   / / /
4(4) , 4(3) , 1(5) , 4(3) , 2 | 54321(5) ‖

CANDYMAN BLUES
By Mississippi John Hurt

Transcribed By Howard Berg

(straight duple meter)

(1)

A6th

G6th   A6th

(10)

G6th   A6th

50

54

St. Louie Tickle

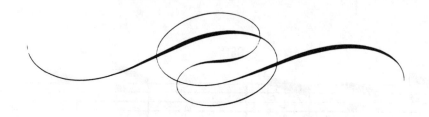

I first heard this ragtime piano tune played
on the radio on the John Davis Show on the guitar on
a phonograph record by Dave
Van Ronk. If you think
that's confusing ... I patterned
my arrangement on a tenor ban-
jo version on a record on
a defunct label on a rainy
day on the way to Encino
on a Tuesday in a Salvation
Army Thrift Store in Canoga
Park, a few miles outside of
Woodland Hills, California. If you think this has
nothing to do with the song, neither does tickling ...
or St. Louie, for that matter.

G

D7th

C

A6th

Chords used in

St. Louie Tickle

A7th

G7th

F

C7th

OPEN

St. Louie Tickle

$$\begin{array}{ccccccc}
/ & & / & / & & & / \\
5 & , & 2 & , & 4 & = & 5 & , & - & , & 2 & , & 4
\end{array}$$

---

(1)

G			D7th		G7th		C		F

$\frac{4}{4}$ 621 , 421 , 521 , 421 | 621 , 421 , 521 , 4 | 62(3) , 2 ,

G			C

43 , 61(0) , 2(3)→(4) , 41(0) | 52 , 3(2) , 3(0) , 4(3) , 4(2) , 4(0) |

5 , 41 , 2(4) , 51 , 2(4) , 41 , 2(4) | 51 , 4(3)1(5) , 51(3) , 4 |

F						C		G

6 , 42 , 3 , 62 , 3 , 42 , 3 | 62 , 41 , 51 , 6(2) | 6(3) ,

(10)

42 , 3(3) , 62 , 3(3) , 42 , 3(3) | 62 , 41 , 61(1) , 43 , 3(2) |

(G)

| / | | / | | / | | / | |
62 , 2(1) , 42(3) , 1(0) , 61(1) , 1(0) , 42(3) , 2(1) | 62 , 3(2) ,

                                C

| / | | / | | / | / | / | | / | | / | |
4 , 3(1) , 63 , 4 | 5 , 41 , 2(4) , 51 , 2(4) , 41 , 2(4) |

                              F

| / | | / | / | / | | / | | / | |
51 , 4(3)1(5) , 51(3) , 4 | 6 , 42 , 3 , 62 , 3 , 42 , 3 |

         C   F   C

| / | / | / | / | / | | / | | / | / |
62 , 41 , 51 , 4 | 62 , 3 , 42 , 2(3) , 6 , 2 , 43 | 51 , 2(4) ,

                                               (20)

     A7th   C7th(2)

| / | / | / | / | | / | | / | | / | | / | |
41 , 41(3) , 3 | 53 , 2 , 41 , 3 , 6(5)2 , 1 , 43 , 2 | 51 ,

D7th   G   OPEN

| / | / | / | repeat | / | | / | | / |
421 , 621 , 4 | from | 4(0)1(7) , 3(0)1(7) , 2(6) , 4(0)1(6) ,
                       beginning

(OPEN)   A6th → A6th(3)

/   /   /   /   /   /

3(0)1(6) , 2(6) | 4(0)1(5) , 3(0)1(5) , 4(0)1(4) , 3(0) , 2 | 43 ,

                                               F(2)   F

/   /   /   /   /   /   /

31(8) , 2 , 41(7) , 31(7) , 2 | 41 , 31 , 41 , 3 | 62 , 3 ,

                           C   A7th   C

/   /   /   /   /   /   /

42 , 2(3) , 6 , 2 , 43 | 51 , 2(4) , 41 , 41(3) , 3 | 51 , 2(4) ,

       G   C   F

/   /   /   /   /   / /   /

41 , 62 , 3(3) , 42 | 52 , 3(2) , 3(0) , 4(2) , 5 , 4 | 6 , 41 ,

(30)

/   /   /   /   /   /   /

61(0) , 42(3) | 62 , 2(0) , 42 , 2(3) , 6 , 2 , 43 | 6 , 41 ,

/   /   /   /   /   /

61(0) , 42(3) | 62 , 2(0) , 42 , 2(3) , 6 , 2 , 43 |

```
C                                                           A7th
  /      /        /        /        /        /        /        /
  5  ,  41 ,  2(4)  ,  51 ,  2(4) ,  41 ,  2(4) │ 51 ,  2(4) ,  41 ,  41(3) ,


    OPEN                                         D7th   G
  /    /        /        /        /        /      /      /      /
  3 │ 2(4) H (5) ,  1 ,  2(3) H (4) ,  1 ,  2(2) H (3) │ 1 ,  421 ,  621 ,  4│
```

PLAY IN STRAIGHT $\frac{4}{4}$ DUPLE METER*

```
              D7th         G7th           C          F
    /       /        /        /        /        /        /        /
{654321 ,  421 ,  521 ,  421 │ 621 ,  421 ,  521 ,  4 │ 62(3) ,  2 ,
```

(40)

```
    G                    C
  /      /        /        /      /      /        /
  43 ,  61(0) ,  2(3)→(4) ,  41(0) │ 52 ,  3(2) ,  3(0) ,  4(3) ,  4(2) ,  4(0)│


  /      /        /        /        /        /        /        /
  5 ,  41 ,  2(4) ,  51 ,  2(4) ,  41 ,  2(4) │ 51 ,  4(3)1(5) ,  51(3) ,  4│


F                                              C          G
  /      /        /        /        /      /      /        /
  6 ,  42 ,  3 ,  62 ,  3 ,  42 ,  3 │ 62 ,  41 ,  51 ,  6(2) │ 6(3) ,
```

* See page 9.

(G)

/   /   /   /   /   /   /

42 , 3(3) , 62 , 3(3) , 42 , 3(3) | 62 , 41 , 61(1) , 43 , 3(2) |

/   /   /   /   /

62 , 2(1) , 42(3) , 1(0) , 61(1) , 1(0) , 42(3) , 2(1) | 62 , 3(2) ,

                                     C

/   /   /   /   /   /   /

4 , 3(1) , 63 , 4 | 5 , 41 , 2(4) , 51 , 2(4) , 41 , 2(4) |

(50)

                                F

/   /   /   /   /   /   /   /

51 , 4(3)1(5) , 51(3) , 4 | 6 , 42 , 3 , 62 , 3 , 42 , 3 |

           C   F   C

/   /   /   /   /   /   /   / /

62 , 41 , 51 , 4 | 62 , 3 , 42 , 2(3) , 6 , 2 , 43 | 51 , 2(4) ,

     A7th   C   G

/   /   / /   /   /   / /   /   / /

41 , 41(3) , 3 | 51 , 2(4) , 41 , 62 , 3(3) , 42 | 52 , 3(2) , 3(0) , 4(2) , 5 , —|

St. Louie Tickle

63

DIGGIN' AND A-FILLIN' RAG

BY ROBERT BAXTER

If you feel the yen to invent your own Finger-Picking piece, this is the tune for you. There are two entire measures ready and waiting for all the inventing you can muster.

I have included three two-bar insertions of my own, but no fair stopping there. Come up with your own. Play kazoo for the insert. Stomp your feet. Yodel. You can even play spoons. Challenge your friends. Show off. Build entire parties around playing the tune. Sponsor a contest. Offer cash prizes. Trips to Hawaii. You will receive my entry via special delivery mail by Friday.

$\times$ = a beat to be filled in by you.

$\downarrow$ = pluck down (thumb)

$\uparrow$ = pluck up (index finger)

Chords used in

Diggin' and a-Fillin' Rag

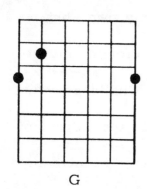

G

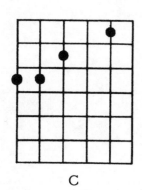

C

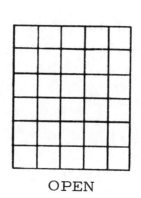

OPEN

spoons

DIGGIN' AND A-FILLIN' RAG
By Robert Baxter

```
 /       /   /           /
 5 , 2 , 4 = 5 , — , 2 , 4
```

_____

(1)

G
```
 /         /        /           /          /    /              /
4 6(2) ||: 6(3) ,  42 , 3(3) ,  62 ,  3 ,  4 | 62 ,  3(3) ,  42 ,  3 ,
4
```

                    C   G
```
 /    /    /     /          /          /    /          /    /      /
 6 ,  5 |  5 ,  41 , 2 ,  61 ,  2 ,  4 | 51 ,  2(4) ,  41 ,  52 ,  6(2) |
```

```
 /          /        /           /          /    /              /        /    /
 6(3) ,  42 , 3(3) ,  62 ,  3 ,  4 | 62 ,  3(3) ,  42 ,  3 ,  6 ,  5 |
```

1.   2.
```
 /    /    /    /    /    /    /    /         /       /         /
 X ,  X ,  X ,  X | X ,  X ,  X ,  X :|| X ,    X ,    5(3) 32 ||
```

In order to lengthen the song, simply play the part
marked with repeat signs more than once.

Continued

Insertion #1

OPEN

2(4) , 1(0) , 2(4) , 1(0) , 2(1) , 3(2) , 3(0) , 4(0)

4(1) <u>P</u> (0) , 5(3) , 4(0) , 5(3) , 6(2)

(damp)

#2

OPEN

1(8) , 1(5) , 2(8) , 1(5) , 2(8) , 1(5) | 2(4) , 2(3) , 2(1) , 2(3) , 2(1) , 6(2)

#3

RHYTHM ON SPOONS

1 - 2 - 3 , 1 - 2 - 3 , 1 - 2 - 3 , 1 - 2 - 3 | 1 - 2 - 3 , 1 - 2 - 3 ,

OPEN

1 - 2 - 3 , 6(2)

DIGGIN' AND A-FILLIN' RAG
By Robert Baxter

Continued

In order to lengthen the song, simply play the part
marked with repeat signs more than once.

Insertion #1

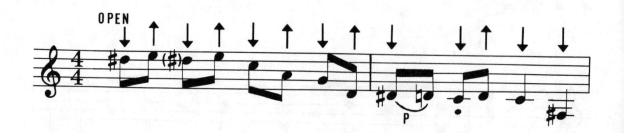

#2

#3

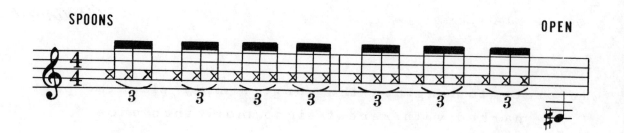

ONE-DIME RAILROAD BLUES

This tune is a combination of Railroad Blues by Sam McGee, and the traditional One-Dime Blues. Railroad Blues can be heard on the Folkways Recording, "The McGee Brothers & Arthur Smith, Vol. 1." I first heard One-Dime Blues played by the marvelous Texas songster, Mance Lipscomb. The excellent version by Etta Baker may also have crept into my arrangement of the tune.

$$3(0) \overset{H}{\frown}, \quad 4\overset{/}{3}(1) \quad = \quad \text{pluck } 3(0) \text{ and hammer-on } 3(1) \text{ so the 2nd}$$

tone sounds out on the beat where the "4" is played normally.

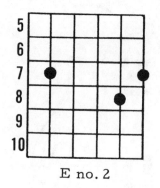

E no. 2

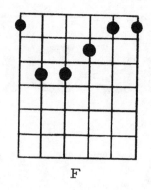

F

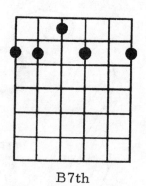

B7th

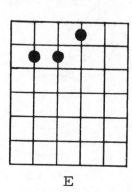

E

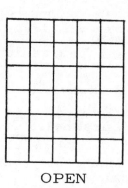

OPEN

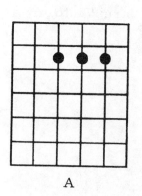

A

Chords used in
One-Dime Railroad Blues

ONE-DIME RAILROAD BLUES

Moderate

(straight duple meter)

(1)

OPEN   E no. 2

$\frac{4}{4}$ 5(2) ➔ 5(7) , 1(7) , 6(0) 2(8S) , 5(7) | 6(0) , 1(7) , 5(7) , 2(8S) ,

6(0) , 1(7) , 5(2) ➔ 5(7) , 1(7) , 6(0) 2(8S) , 5(7) | 6(0) , 1(7) ,

F(4)

5(7) , 2(8S) , 6(0) , 1(7) , 5(7) | 6 , 2 , 4 , 1 , 6 , 2 , 4 |

E no. 2

6 , 2 , 4 , 1 , 6 , 2 , 5(2) ➔ 5(7) , 1(7) , 6(0) 2(8S) , 5(7) |

6(0) , 1(7) , 5(7) , 2(8S) , 6(0) , 1(7) , 5(2) ➔ 5(7) , 1(7) ,

(10)

(E no. 2)

```
          /              /       /         /              /           /
6(0)2(8S) , 5(7) | 6(0) , 1(7) , 5(7) , 2(8S) , 6(0) , 1(7) , 5(7) |
```

B7th   B7th(1)   B7th   E

```
 /         /       /       /       /       /    /         /       /      /   /
 5 ,  1 ,  4 ,  2 ,  5 ,  1 ,  4 | 5 ,  1 ,  4 ,  5 ,  1 ,  4 | 61 ,
```

                                                              A

```
 /    /        H   /       /       /       /       /
 4 ,  6 ,  3(0) , 43(1) | 61 ,  4 ,  6 ,  4 | 52(0) H (2) ,  4 ,  1 ,
```

                                                              E

```
 /         /         /           /       /       /       /    /
 5 ,  2 ,  4 ,  1(3) | 5 ,  1(2) ,  4 ,  1 ,  5 ,  2 ,  4 | 6 ,
```

```
   /          H             /      /          H           /         /                /              /
43(0) H (1) ,  6 ,  43(0) H (1) | 6 ,  43(0) H (1) ,  62(3) ,  4 |
```

(20)

A

```
   /                    /       /       /                /         /         /    /
52(0) H (2) ,  4 ,  1 ,  5 ,  2 ,  4 ,  1(3) | 5 ,  1(2) ,  4 ,  1 ,  5 ,  2 ,  4 |
```

E
/   /   /   /   /   /   /   /
6 , 43(0) H (1) , 6 , 43(0) H (1) | 6 , 43(0) H (1) , 61(4) , 4 |

B7th(2)   OPEN   B7th   E
/   /   /   /   /   /   /   /   /
5 , 1 , 4 , 61 , 4 | 51 , 4 , 61 , 4 , 3(0) H (1) | 6 , 2 ,

                              B7th(2)   OPEN   B7th   E
/   /   /   /   /   /   /   /   /   /   /   /
4 , 61 , 4 | 61(4) , 4 , 5 , 1 , 4 | 61 , 4 , 51 , 4 | 61 ,

                        (30)

                                            A
/   /   /   /   /   /   /   /
4 , 3(0) H (1) , 6 , 2 , 4 | 61 , 4 , 6 , 2(3) , 4 | 52(0) H (2) ,

/   /   /   /   /   /   /
4 , 1 , 5 , 2 , 4 , 1(3) | 5 , 1(2) , 4 , 1 , 5 , 2 , 4 |

E
/   /   /   /   /   /   /   /
6 , 43(0) H (1) , 6 , 43(0) H (1) | 6 , 43(0) H (1) , 61(4) , 4 |

B7th(2)   OPEN   B7th   E

/   /   /   /   /   /   /   /

5 , 1 , 4 , 61 , 4 | 51 , 4 , 61 , 4 , 3(0) H (1) | 6 , 2 ,

/   /   /   /   B7th(2)   OPEN   B7th

4 , 61 , 4 | 61(4) , 4 , 5 , 1 , 4 | 61 , 4 , 51 , 4 |

(40)

E

/   /   /   /   /   /

61 , 4 , 3(0) H (1) , 6 , 2 , 4 | 61 , 4 , 6 , 2(3) ,

E no. 2

/   /   /   /   /   /   /

5(2) → 5(7) , 1(7) , 6(0)2(8S) , 5(7) | 6(0) , 1(7) , 5(7) , 2(8S) ,

/   /   /   /   /   /   /

6(0) , 1(7) , 5(2) → 5(7) , 1(7) , 6(0)2(8S) , 5(7) | 6(0) , 1(7) ,

F(4)

/   /   /   /   /   /   /   /

5(7) , 2(8S) , 6(0) , 1(7) , 5(7) | 6 , 2 , 4 , 1 , 6 , 2 , 4 |

(F(4))   E no.2
 /   /   /   /   /   /   /   /   /   /   /
 6 , 2 , 4 , 1 , 6 , 2 , 5(2)──► 5(7) , 1(7) , 6(0)2(8S) , 5(7) |

 /   /   /   /   /   /   /   /   /
 6(0) , 1(7) , 5(7) , 2(8S) , 6(0) , 1(7) , 5(2)──► 5(7) , 1(7) ,

                 (50)

     /   /   /   /   /   /   /   /
 6(0)2(8S) , 5(7) | 6(0) , 1(7) , 5(7) , 2(8S) , 6(0) , 1(7) , 5(7) |

B7th   B7th(1)   B7th
 /   /   /   /   /   /   /   /   /
 5 , 1 , 4 , 2 , 5 , 1 , 4 | 5 , 1 , 4 , 5 , 1 , 4 |

E
   /   /   /   H   /   /   /   /   /   /
 61 , 4 , 6 , 3(0) ⌒ , 43(1) | 61 , 4 , 6 , 4 | 63(0) H (1) ,

   /   /   /   /   /   /
 41 , 63(0) H (1) , 42(3S) | ─ , ─ , ─ ‖

ONE-DIME RAILROAD BLUES

Moderate

(straight duple meter)

(20)

(30)

WINDING BOY

Winding Boy is derived directly from Ian Buchanan's perform-
ance on the record "The Blues Project" (Elektra Records - EKL264.)
The first-time-through melody is mainly Ian's, while the improvisations
are my own, based on the beautiful chord progressions and melodies
of the original.

Unlike the other triple-meter pieces in this manual, the music
notation (not the tablature) of Winding Boy uses no shorthand symbol to
indicate the triplet timing (see pg. 11.) Instead, the music is written out
in full (using ♪♪♪ instead of ♪♪ .) It might be good to remind you that
♪♪♪ is a proper way to write a triplet. The quarter note being twice
the value of the eighth note. Perhaps the clutter of triplets will illus-
trate why a timing symbol is used throughout the rest of this manual.

The tablature and the music both use a standard music symbol
"2nd Time To Coda," which means, play the piece from the beginning,
all the way to the repeat sign (:|); then go back to the first page where
you find a repeat sign facing the opposite direction (|:); play from this
repeat sign all the way through the measure marked "2nd Time To Coda;"
now go directly to the section at the end of the piece marked "CODA."
"CODA" means "end."

D7th

A6th

G

A7th

C

A♭6th

OPEN

Dm

E

Chords used in Winding Boy

WINDING BOY

Based On an Arrangement
By Ian Buchanan

Slow and deliberate

/　　　　/　　　　/　　　　　　　　/
5 , 2 , 4 = 5 , — , 2 , 4

(1)

D7th(5)　　　　　　　G

4/4　/　　　　　　　　　/　　　　　/　　　　　　　　　　　/
31 , 1(5) ‖: 3 , 2 , 61 , 5(0) , 5(1) , 5(2) , 6(3) , 1 |

A6th ⟶ A6th(3)　　　　　　　　G

/　　　　　/　　　　　　　　/　　　　　　　/
41(1) , 2 , 42 , 1(8) , 41(6) , 2 , 61 , 1(1) | 42(3)⟶(4) ,

C

　　　/　　　　　　　　/　　　　　　　　　　/
1(0) , 52 , 2(3)⟶(5) , 4(0)1(3) H (5) , 1(3) , 5(0)2(4) H (5) , 1(3) |

A7th(1) C　　　　　D7th(5)　　　　　G

/　　　　/　　/　　/　　　　　　　/　　　　　/　　　　　/
52 , 3 , 42 , 2 , 5 , 4 , 2(0) | 31 , 1(5) , 3 , 2 , 61 , 5(0) ,

A6th⟶A6th(3)

/　　　　　　　/　　　　　　　　/　　　　　　/
5(1) , 5(2) | 6(3) , 1 , 41(1) , 2 , 42 , 1(8) , 41(6) , 2 |

G   C

/   /   /   /

61 , 1(1) , 42(3)→(4) , 1(0) , 52 , 2(3)→(5) , 4(0)1(3) H (5) ,

                                       A7th(1) C

/   /   /   / /   /   /

1(3) | 5(0)2(4) H (5) , 1(3) , 52 , 3 , 42 , 2 , 5 | 4 , 6(3) , 4 ,

(10)

Ab6th→A6th(7)

            /   /   /   /

2 , 4 , 1(12) | 31(12) , 1(12) , 41(10) , 1(12) , 3 , 2(0) ,

Ab6th→A6th   Ab6th→A6th

/   /   /   /

42 , 3 | 4(0)2(0) , 3 , 5(4) , 5 , 4 , 5 , 42 , 3 |

                                                 Dm

/   /   /   /

4(0)2(0) , 3 , 5(4) , 5 , 4 , 5 , 5(4) , 4 , 1 | 31 , 1 ,

                                                 G

/   /   /   /   /   /   /

41(0) , 2 , 3 , 2 , 51 , 1(0) | 4 , 2 , 5 , 1 , 6(0) , 6(2) , 6 , 1 |

(G)

/   /   /   /
41 , 1 , 61(1) , 1 , 4 , 2(3)→(4) , 41(0) , 1(3) | 31(0) , 1(3) ,

2nd Time To Coda|

C   A7th(1) C   OPEN

/   /   /   /   /
52 , 3 , 42 , 2 , 5 | 4(3)2(4) , 1 , 4(4)2(1) , 3 , 4(3)2(0) , 2(1) ,

C   D7th(5)   G

/ /   /   /   /   /
5 | 4 , 2(0) , 31 , 1(5) , 3 , 2(0) , 61 , 5(0) | 5(1) H (2) , 4 ,

(20)

                                          C

/   /   /   /
6 , 41 , 61(1) , 2(4) , 41(0) , 52 , 2(3)→(5) | 4(0)1(3) H (5) , 1(3) ,

                     A7th(1)   C   D7th(5)

/   /   /   / /   /
2(4S) , 1 , 5 , 2 , 4 , 42 , 1(0) , 2 | 5 , 4 , 2(0) , 31 , 1(5) ,

         G

/   /   /   /   /
3 , 2(0) | 61 , 5(0) , 5(1) H (2) , 4 , 6 , 41 , 61(1) , 2(4) , 41(0) |

89

```
 C            A7th(1)       A7th(2)       A7th(3)      C           OPEN
 /            /             /             /            /           /
52  ,  1  ,  42  ,  1(0) ,  42  ,  1(0) ,  42  ,  1(0) | 52  ,  1  ,  4(3)2(4)  ,  1  ,
```

```
                                             C                       E
   /              /                          /      /       /      /        /
4(4)2(1)  ,  3  ,  4(3)2(0)  ,  2(1) | 5  ,  4  ,  6(3)  ,  4  ,  2(3) | 6  ,  1  ,
```

```
                                    Ab6th → A6th
 /              /                          /                                /
41  ,  1  ,  62(0) H (3) ,  1  ,  4  ,  2  |  4  ,  3  ,  2  ,  4(0)2(0)  ,
```

```
                                Ab6th ──→ A6th
        /           /                    /                     /                   /
3  ,  2(0)  ,  43  ,  5  ,  4(0) | 42  ,  3  ,  4(0)2(0)  ,  3  ,  2(0)  ,  53  ,
```

(30)

```
        Dm            /        /                  /              /          /              /
 /                                                                                         
 4  ,  4 | 31  ,  31  ,  2  ,  51(0)  ,  2  ,  4  ,  2 | 51  ,  1(0)  ,  4  ,  2  ,
```

```
                     G
 /           /              /              /                  /                  /
 5  ,  1  ,  4  ,  6(2) | 6  ,  1  ,  41  ,  1  ,  61(1) H (3)  ,  1  ,  4  ,  2 |
```

90

(G)   C   A7th(2) → A7th(1)

/   /   /   /

61(1) H̲ (3) , 1(1) , 42(3) → (4) , 1(0) , 5 , 2 , 4 , 42   ,   1(0) |

C   G   C

/   /   /   /   /   /   /

52 , 3 , 4 , 3 , 6 , 1 , 42(3) → (4) , 1(0) | 52 , 4 , 5 ,

                                         CODA

      D7th(5)   OPEN

         /   /   /   /

2(0) , 31 , 1(5) :‖ 4(3)2(4) , 1 , 4(4)2(1) , 3 , 4(3)2(0) ,

      C

      /   /   /   /

2(1) , 5 | — , — , — ‖

WINDING BOY

Based On An Arrangement
By Ian Buchanan

Slow and deliberate

92

(30)

94

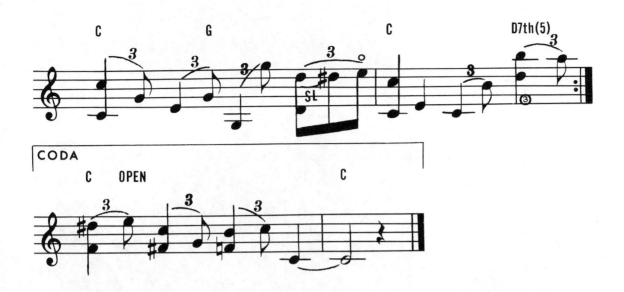

CODA

CANDYCANE MAN

Of all the songs in this manual, the following tune is not the most complicated, longest or hardest to master ... but it certainly is the most unusual. The bass-line is backward!

This does not mean, however, that a normal treble string melody is simply played over a new-type bass-line. That would only make the song harder to play for no apparent reason. Rather, the backward bass-line is used to lend musical interest to a song that otherwise would be uninteresting. The specific backward bass-line used in this song is so unusual and important that the simple melody comes to life only because of it.

It might occur to you that a backward bass-line would sound like a normal forward bass-line by the third note:

$$/ \quad / \quad /$$
$$4 \quad , \quad 5 \quad , \quad 4 \quad , \quad . \quad . \quad .$$

normal forward pattern

To avoid this confusion, the backward bass-line in <u>Candycane Man</u> is

$$/ \quad / \quad / \quad /$$
"3 , 5 , 3(2) , 5 ." (<u>This pattern is played with the thumb.</u>)

The 3rd string, because it is not usually played in a constant bass pattern, tends to stand out, especially when it is fretted at the 2nd fret every other time. This makes it sound as if it is leading off the pattern, which is the effect you are after.

Now that you have straightened this out in your mind, a monkey-wrench is thrown into the works ... the 17th, 18th, and 19th measures are played with a normal forward bass line. This is done to further point out, by comparison, that the rest of the song uses the backward bass-line.

The most difficult part of using both a backward and forward bass-line in the same song is the developing of a smooth transition between the two contrasting patterns. In this tune it is accomplished by playing the 6th string twice in a row:

```
 /      /      /        /    /      /
 3  ,   5  ,   3(2)  ,  6(0) | 6  ,  4  ,  .  .  .
```
6th string played
twice

To get back into the backward bass-line, a bass pattern of
```
/   /   /   /
"5 , 6 , 4 , 5"
```
is played which makes this transition, like the one a few measures earlier, both smooth and pleasing to the ear.

The ideas and the melody for this tune are taken from the playing of <u>Candyman</u> by Rev. Gary Davis, Jack Elliot and Erik Darling; versions quite different than John Hurt's, given earlier in this manual.

Chords used in Candycane Man

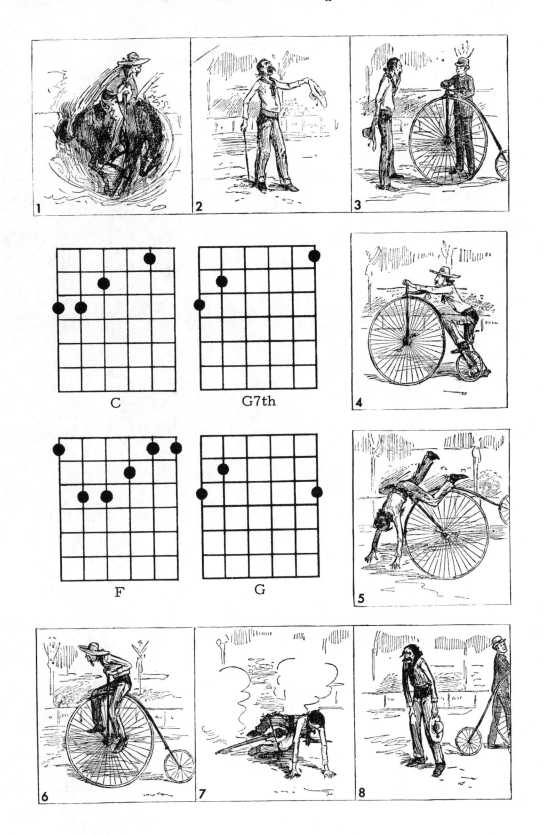

C

G7th

F

G

CANDYCANE MAN

Slow and deliberate

```
/         /     /              /
5  ,  2 ,  4  =  5  ,  —  ,  2  ,  4
```

_____

(1)

C

$\frac{4}{4}$
```
 /     /       /        /   /              /        /    /     /      /        /
 3 ,  5 ,  3(2) ,  5 | 3 ,  2 ,  5 ,  3(2) ,  5 | 3 ,  5 ,  3(2) ,  5 |
```

                                    C
```
 /       /      /        /    /       /                /     /
 3  ,  2 ,  5 ,  3(2) ,  5 | 31 ,  51 ,  2 ,  3(2)1 ,  1(3) ,  5 | 3 ,  2 ,
```

```
 /       /       /    /       /        /              /   /       /     /       /
 5 ,  3(2) ,  5 | 31 ,  51 ,  3(2)2(3) ,  2 ,  5 | 3 ,  2 ,  5 ,  3(2) ,  5 |
```

                                    (10)

G7th   C
```
 /      /        /          /   /      /       /         /   /       /
 31 ,  61 ,  3(2)1 ,  1(3) ,  6 | 3 ,  2 ,  6 ,  3(2) ,  6 | 31 ,  51 ,
```

```
 /             /    /       /            /              /   /       /
 3(2)2(3) ,  2 ,  5 | 32(1) H (3) ,  1 ,  2 ,  3(2) P (0) ,  5 | 31 ,  51 ,
```

(C)

     /   / /   /   /   / /   /   /

2 , 3(2)1 , 1(3) , 5 | 3 , 2 , 5 , 3(2) , 5 | 31 , 51 , 3(2)2(3) ,

                                         F

          / /   /   /   /   /   /   /   /

2 , 5 | 3 , 2 , 5 , 3(2) , 6(0) | 6(1)2 , 2 , 4 , 6(2)2(3) , 4 |

C   G

   /   /   /   /   /   /   /   /

6(3)2 , 1 , 4 , 6(3)1(3) , 4 | 61 , 41(1) , 63(2) , 2 , 4 |

(20)

C

 /   /   /   /

52 , 6(3) , 4 , 5 ‖

CANDYCANE MAN

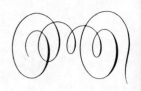

Slow and deliberate

(1) C

(10)
G7th   C

(20)
F   C   G   C

102

EARLY MORNING

BLUES

BY ARTHUR "BLIND" BLAKE

This slow-rocking Blind Blake piece fills an important position in this collection. It is the tune that my wife likes best.

See note regarding repeat signs and coda in Winding Boy.

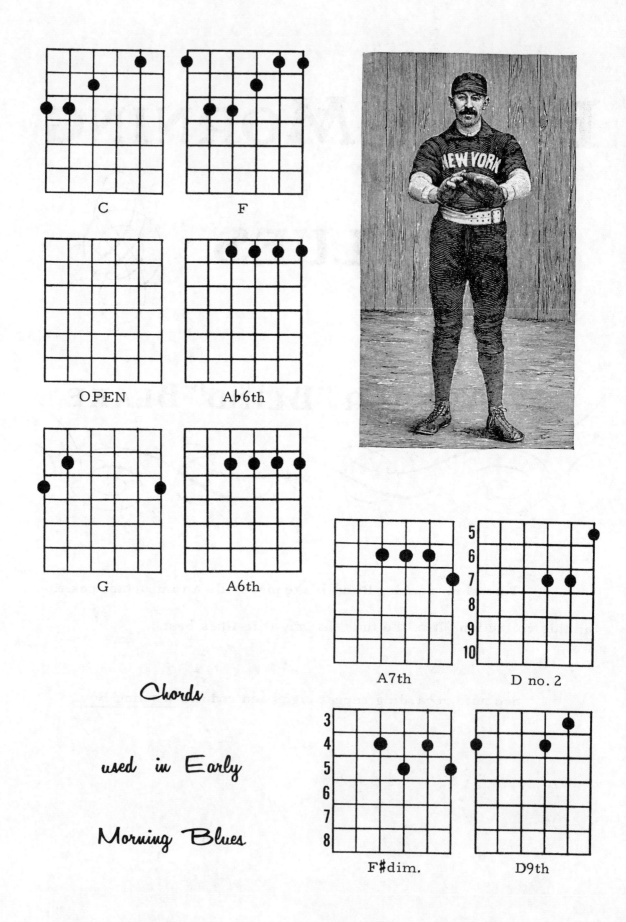

C   F

OPEN   Ab6th

G   A6th

A7th   D no. 2

F#dim.   D9th

Chords

used in Early

Morning Blues

EARLY MORNING BLUES

By Blind Blake

Moderate

```
 /        /     /              /
 5  ,  2  ,  4   =   5  ,  —  ,  2  ,  4
```

(1)

C   F

$\frac{4}{4}$ 6(3) , 5(0) , 5(2) ‖: 5(3) , 1(3) , 4 , 1(5) , 51(3) , 2 , 4 , 3 |

                         G   C

61 , 1(3) , 1 , 42 , 3 , 63 , 1 , 4(0)2(3)→(5) , 1(0) | 52 ,

   G   C

3 , 61 , 1(5) , 1 , 41(1) , 2(3) , 2 , 63 , 3(2) , 2 | 51 ,

                                                 F

2(4) , 1 , 42 , 3 , 3(2) , 53(3) , 4 , 3 | 61 , 1 , 4 , 1(3) ,

                                                  G

61 , 2 , 4 | 61 , 1(0) , 41 , 1(2) , 1(3) , 6 , 1(1) , 4(0)2(3)→(5) , 1(0) |

C G C
/ / / /
52 , 3 , 61 , 1(5) , 1 , 41(1) , 2(3) , 2 , 63 , 3(2) , 2 |

A♭6th ⟶ A6th OPEN
/ / / /
51 , 1(3) , 4(0)2(3) ⟶ (5) , 1(0) , 42 , 3 , 5 , 2(3) ⟶ 2(7) |

(10)

D no. 2 F(2)
/ / / / /
41 , 1 , 3 , 1(8) , 41(7) P (5) , 2 , 3 , 2 | 61 , 1(5) , 1 ,

C A7th(1) C G
/ / / / /
42(5S) , 1(0) , 52 , 3 , 42 , 2 | 5 , 3 , 61 , 1(5) , 1 ,

2nd Time To Coda
C
/ / / /
41(1) , 2(3) , 2 , 63 , 3(2) , 2 | 51 , 2(4) , 1 , 42 , 3 , 3(2) ,

/ / / / / /
52 , 4 | 51(3) , 1(3) , 4 , 1(5) , 51(3) , 5(2) , 4(0) , 5(0) |

```
F                 Ab6th           D9th        G              C
/                  /               /          /              /
41 , 1(3) , 1 , 42 , 1(0) , 62 , 3 , 62(3) , 1(0) , 2 | 5 , 3 ,


G                                              C
/                  /               /           /
61 , 1(5) , 1 , 41(1) , 2(3) , 2 , 63 , 3(2) , 2 | 51 , 2(4) , 1 ,


/                  /                           /
42 , 3 , 3(2) , 5 , 2 , — , 4 , 2(0) , — , 53(3) , 2 , 3(3) |


F                              F#dim.
/      /       /       /        /       /
6 , 1 , 4 , 1(3) , 61 , 2 , 4 , 3 | 421 , 1 , 3 , 2 ,


G                       C        G
/          /                     /            /
61 , 1(1) , 4(0)2(3)→(5) | 52 , 3 , 61 , 1(5) , 1 , 41(1) , 2(3) , 2 ,


            (20)

            C                          Ab6th→A6th       D9th
/           /             /             /               /
63 , 3(2) , 2 | 51 , 1(3) , 4(0)2(3)→(5) , 1(0) , 42 , 3 , 5 , 6(0) |
```

(D9th)

/   /   /   /   G
6 , 2 , 4 , 3 , 62(1) P (0) , 3 , 4 , 6(2) | 6 , 1 , 4 , 5(1) ,

                     C   G
/   /   /   /   /
5(2) , 1 , 4 , 5(2) | 5 , 2 , 61 , 1(5) , 1 , 41(1) , 2(3) , 2 ,

          C
/   /   /   /   /
63 , 3(2) , 2 | 51 , 2(4) , 1 , 2 , 3 , 3(2) , 52 , 4 :‖

CODA

/   /   /   /   /   /   /
51 , 2(4) , 1 , 42 , 3 , 3(2) , 52 , 5 , 43(3) | — , — , —‖

108

EARLY MORNING BLUES
By Blind Blake

THE
RAMBLING BOY

Here is an interesting example of what happens when a light, breezy old English folk melody meets face to face with a ragtime Negro guitar style.

Take the melody, send it across the sea, make it familiar through the singing of such diverse artists as the Carter Family and Joan Baez, bend it to fit the guitar styling of a sort of John Hurt-Blind Boy Fuller - Elizabeth Cotten - Rev. Gary Davis - Dick Rosmini - Etta Baker - Ry Cooder - Sam McGee conglomeration and you have a Folk Process arrangement.

When fine old tunes are subjected to the Folk Process they usually suffer. Hopefully we have broken this rule.

To play The Rambling Boy lower the 6th string one whole note to D, and refer to Policedog Blues (page 28) regarding the playing of harmonics.

$$\overset{H}{1(0)} , \overset{/}{41(2)} = $$ pluck "1(0)," as noted, and hammer-on "1(2)" so that this second tone of the hammer-on falls on the same beat as the "4." The "4" is plucked by the thumb as usual.

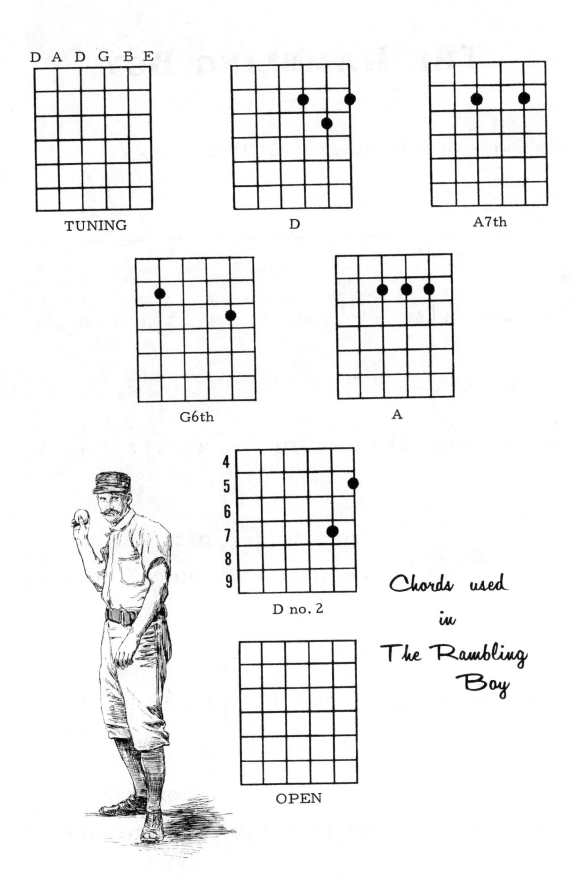

D A D G B E

TUNING

D

A7th

G6th

A

4
5
6
7
8
9

D no. 2

OPEN

Chords used in The Rambling Boy

113

THE RAMBLING BOY

guitar tuning (6th to 1st string): D A D G B E

```
 /       /   /           /
5 , 2 , 4  =  5 , — , 2 , 4
```

_____

(1)

D
```
  /              /     /      /     /        /      /
4 63 , 2(0) , 4 | 62 , 4 , 5(2) , 2 , 4 , 3 | 6 , 41 , 2 ,
4
```

```
    /         /           /   /    /        /      /
61(0) , 2 , 42(0) , 2 | 6 , 4 , 5(2) , 2 , 4 , 3 | 6 , 41 , 2 ,
```

```
                                                    OPEN
  /           H   /      /              /        /                 /
61 , 1(0) ⌒ 41(2) | 61(5) , 1(5) , 4 , 6(5)1(5) , 1(5) , 4 |
```

```
                                           A7th        G6th
     /        /      /              /     /    /    /   /
6(4)1(5) , 1(5) , 4 , 6(2)1(5) , 1(0) , 4 , 2 | 5 , 4 , 5 , 3 , 2 ,
```

```
   A7th       D
  /  /     /     /      H   /      /              /        /     /
4 | 52 , 4 , 61 , 1(0) ⌒ 41(2) | 61(5) , 1(5) , 4 , 5(4)1(5) , 1(5) , 4 |
                                                          OPEN
```

(10)

(OPEN)   D   G6th

/   /   /   /   /   /   /

5(2)1(5) , 1(5) , 4 , 61 , 2 , 41(0) , 3 | 5 , 4 , 52 , 1 ,

                              A   G6th   A

/   /   /   /   / /   /   /   /

4 , 3 | 5 , 4 , 52 , 1 , 4 | 53 , 2 , 4 , 5 , 42 , 1 , 4 , 3 |

                                    D   G6th

/   /   /   /   / / /

5 , 41(2) , 2(0) , 51(0) , 2 , 4(0)1(0) , 2 | 6 , 4 , 5 , 2 , 1 ,

    D

/   /   /   /   /   /   /   /

4 , 2 | 6 , 4 , 63 , 2(0) , 4 , 2 | 6 , 4 , 6 , 6(2) , 5 , 5(2) |

/   /   /   /   /   /   /   /

4 , 31 , 2 , 61(0) , 2 , 42(0) , 2 | 6 , 4 , 6 , 6(2) , 5 , 5(2) |

(20)

                                D no. 2

/   /   /   H /   /   /   /   /

4 , 31 , 2 , 61 , 1(0) , 41(2) | 61(5) , 1(5) , 4 , 6 , 2(7) , 4 , 1(5) |

115

(D no. 2)   A7th
  /   /   /   /   /   /   /   /
  6   ,   41(5) ,   2(6) ,   1(0) ,   3(7) ,   2(0) , 3(0) | 52   ,   4 ,

G6th   A7th   D
  /   /   /   /   /   /   H /
  5 , 3 , 2 , 4 , 3 , 2(0) | 52 , 41 , 2 , 61 , 1(0) , 41(2) |

D no. 2
  /   /   /   /   /   /   /
  61(5) , 1(5) , 4 ,   6 , 2(7) , 4 , 1(5) | 6 ,   41(5) , 2(6) , 1(0) , 3(7) ,

              G6th   A
  /   /   /   /   /   /   /   /   /
  2(0) , 3(0) | 52 , 4 , 52 , 1 , 42 , 3 | 5 , 4 , 52 , 1 , 42 , 3 |

                          (30)

              G6th   A
  /   /   /   /   /   /   /
  5 , 4 , 5 , 3 , 2 , 4 , 3 | 52 , 41(2) , 2 , 51(0) , 2 , 41(0) |

                        HARM. (7)
D   HARM. (12)   D
  /   /   /   /   /   /   /   /
  62   ,   4   ,   432   ,   432 | 632   ,   4   ,   63   ,   2(0)   ,   4   ,   3 |

(D)   HARM.(12)   HARM.(7)

                               D

/   /   /   /   /   /   /

62 , 4 , 3 , 2 , 4 , 432 | 632 , 41 , 2 , 61(0) , 2 , 42(0) ,

                               HARM.(7)

             HARM.(12)   D   H

       /   /   /   /   /   /   /

2 | 6 , 4 , 3 , 2 , 4 , 432 | 632 , 41 , 2 , 61 , 1(0) , 41(2) |

             OPEN

/   /   /   /   /   /

61(5) , 1(5) , 4 , 6(5)1(5) , 4 | 6(4)1(5) , 1(5) , 4 , 6(2)1(5) ,

(40)

      A7th   G6th   A7th   D

       /   /   /   /   /   /   /   /   H   /

1(0) , 4 , 2 | 5 , 4 , 5 , 3 , 2 , 4 | 52 , 4 , 61 , 1(0) , 41(2) |

             OPEN   D

/   /   /   /   /   /

61(5) , 1(5) , 4 , 5(4)1(5) , 1(5) , 4 | 5(2)1(5) , 4 , 61 , 2 ,

       G6th

/   /   /   /   /   /   /   /   /

41(0) , 3 | 5 , 4 , 52 , 1 , 4 , 3 | 5 , 4 , 52 , 1 , 4 |

A G6th A
/ / / / / / /
53 , 2 , 4 , 5 , 42 , 1 , 4 , 3 | 5 , 41(2) , 2(0) , 51(0) ,

D G6th D
/ / / / / //
2 , 41(0) , 2 | 6 , 4 , 5 , 2 , 1 , 4 , 3 | 62 ||

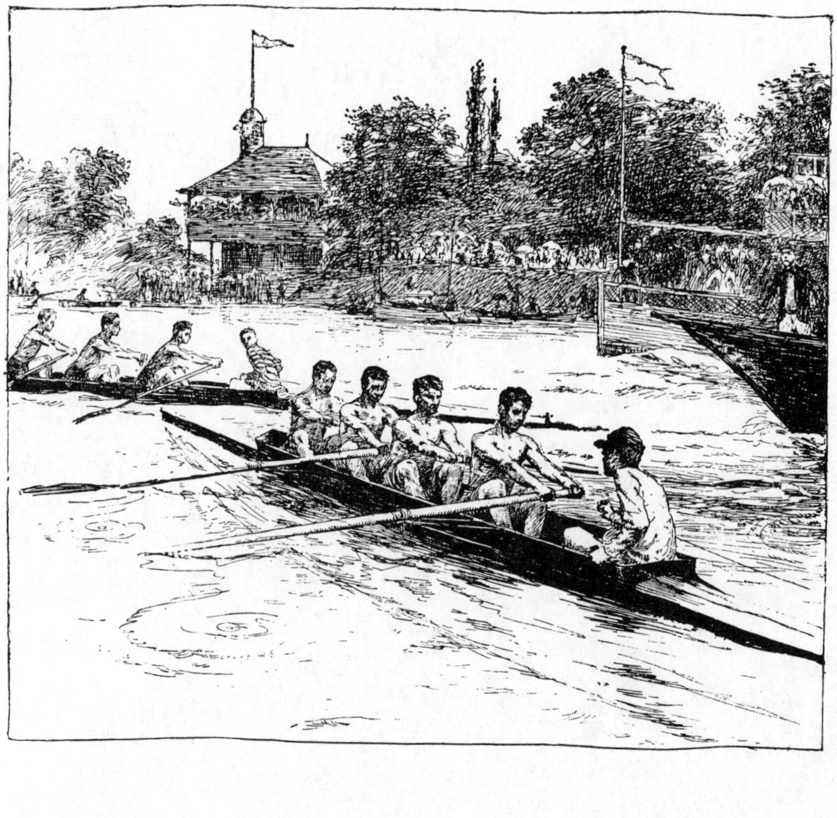

THE RAMBLING BOY

guitar tuning (6th to 1st string): D A D G B E